C000193746

Drum Kit 2

Pieces & Exercises

for Trinity College London exams
2014–2019

Grades 3 & 4

Published by
Trinity College London Press
trinitycollege.com

Registered in England
Company no. 09726123

Copyright © 2013 Trinity College London
Third impression, March 2017

Music processed by Scott Barnard.
Printed in England by Caligraving Ltd.

Trinity College London graded drum kit exams

Introduction

The aim of the Trinity College London drum kit syllabus is the development of versatile musicians, confident to play with authority, creativity and sensitivity across a broad range of styles and able to read and interpret drum charts with conviction and flair.

Drum kit exams

Candidates are required to perform:

- two exercises. The first is chosen by the candidate, the other is chosen by the examiner from the remaining two exercises.
- two pieces from group A (played with a backing track, with or without click, or live piano accompaniment)
- one piece from group B (unaccompanied)
- two supporting tests

Exercises are specially written pieces that involve all the rudiments set for a particular grade (see cumulative rudiments grid). These rudiments are set out at the beginning of each grade section. Candidates will be required to learn these in order to be able to play the exercises.

Group A pieces have full backing accompaniment on CD, with and without click track, or piano accompaniment where appropriate. Candidates will be marked on their ability to interpret a typical drum chart and interact with the backing in terms of time-keeping, phrasing, soloing etc.

Group B pieces are unaccompanied.

Supporting tests explore the candidate's perception and broader knowledge.

For full details on how to enter for an exam, venue equipment, supporting tests and how the exams are assessed, please refer to the current syllabus booklet which can be found at www.trinitycollege.com

Drum kit rudiments

Rudiment	Grade 1	Grade 2	Grade 3	Grade 4	Grade 5	Grade 6	Grade 7	Grade 8
Single stroke roll	✓	✓	✓	✓	✓	✓	✓	✓
Double stroke roll	✓	✓	✓	✓	✓	✓	✓	✓
Single paradiddle	✓	✓	✓	✓	✓	✓	✓	✓
Flam		✓	✓	✓	✓	✓	✓	✓
Drag		✓	✓	✓	✓	✓	✓	✓
Four stroke ruff		✓	✓	✓	✓	✓	✓	✓
Five stroke roll			✓	✓	✓	✓	✓	✓
Seven stroke roll			✓	✓	✓	✓	✓	✓
Nine stroke roll			✓	✓	✓	✓	✓	✓
Flam tap				✓	✓	✓	✓	✓
Flam accent				✓	✓	✓	✓	✓
Flamacue				✓	✓	✓	✓	✓
Flam paradiddle				✓	✓	✓	✓	✓
Double paradiddle				✓	✓	✓	✓	✓
Paradiddle-diddle				✓	✓	✓	✓	✓
Drag and stroke					✓	✓	✓	✓
Double drag and stroke					✓	✓	✓	✓
Drag paradiddle					✓	✓	✓	✓
Single ratamacue					✓	✓	✓	✓
Double ratamacue					✓	✓	✓	✓
Triple ratamacue					✓	✓	✓	✓
Triple paradiddle						✓	✓	✓
Reverse paradiddle						✓	✓	✓
Pata fla fla							✓	✓
Swiss army triplet							✓	✓
Inward paradiddle							✓	✓

Drum kit notation key

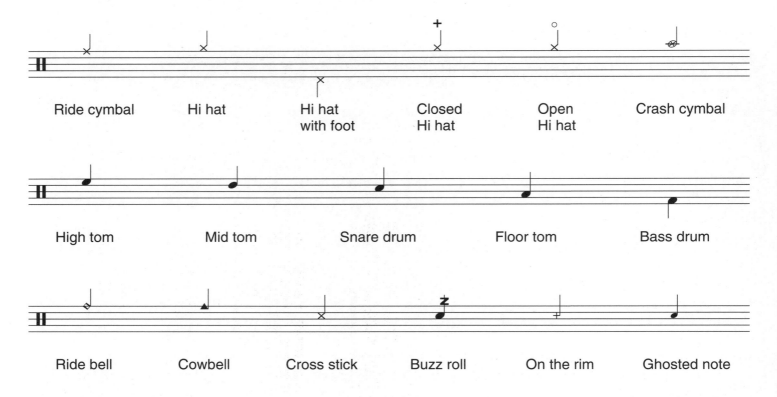

Ride cymbal | Hi hat | Hi hat with foot | Closed Hi hat | Open Hi hat | Crash cymbal

High tom | Mid tom | Snare drum | Floor tom | Bass drum

Ride bell | Cowbell | Cross stick | Buzz roll | On the rim | Ghosted note

Please note that the notation used for ride cymbal (and bell), crash cymbal and cross stick has changed from that used in previous Trinity College London exam publications. Drum kit notation varies between different publishers/arrangers but the key above is becoming more consistently used.

Recording credits

Need I Remind You?	Vocals, Piano, Bass: Adam Double, Guitars: Ross Chapman, Drums: George Double
Party People	Vocal: Iain Hornal, Backing vocals: Victoria Beaumont & Adeola Shyllon, Trumpets: Jean-Paul Gervasoni & Owain Harries, Saxes: Mike Lesirge & Erica Clarke Trombone: Alan Hardiman, Keys: Dave Holland, Guitar: Ryan Haberfield, Bass: Vinzenz Benjamin, Percussion: Craig Mathewson, Drums: Matt McDonough
Reggae Muffin	Guitar & Bass: Enrico Pinna, Drums: Matt McDonough
Way Cool	Arrangements & Keyboards: Richard Cottle, Guitar: Adam Goldsmith, Bass Guitar: Laurence Cottle, Percussion: Danny Cummings, Drums: Ralph Salmins
The Chicken	Trumpets: Jonnie Bruce, Sax: Alfred 'Pee Wee' Ellis, Organ: Anders Olinder, Guitar: Jerry Crozier, Drums & Percussion: Andrew Tween
Soul Bossa Nova	Piccolo, Flute, Saxes: Gemma Moore, Piano: Chris Ingham, Bass: Arnie Somogyi, Drums: George Double
Soul Station	Piano: Chris Ingham, Sax: Gemma Moore, Bass: Arnie Somogyi, Drums: George Double
The Spark, The Flame	Guitar, Keyboard, Bass, Programming: Andy Staples, Drums: Pete Riley

Recorded at various locations. Recordings co-ordinated and mastered by Mark Rogers.

Performance notes

General note for both grades

Where a crash cymbal appears at the start of a bar and is followed by one-bar repeat signs (⟦ 𝄍 ⟧), the crash cymbal should **not** be played in the repeat bars. If a crash cymbal is required, it will be notated above the repeated bar in question. This is universally accepted as standard drum kit notation and it is the aim of the Trinity College London syllabus to encourage students to become familiar with what they will be confronted with in the real world of drum kit performance.

All repeats, including those within *da capo* and *dal segno* sections, should be observed in drum kit exams.

Candidates may use the backing track with or without clicks in the exam.

Grade 3

Dave Odart   Exercise no. 1

This exercise combines a straight 8s rock groove with semiquaver/sixteenth note paradiddles. Count carefully to ensure that the various fill durations do not cause you to misjudge the bar length. Maintain a relaxed feel throughout and be careful not to change the tempo during the crescendos. Listen to the playing of David Garibaldi for examples of this style.

Dave Odart   Exercise no. 2

Influenced by traditional Celtic/Irish music, this exercise should be performed as a jig with the snares off. Pay careful attention to the left hand strokes during the opening rhythm to ensure that only the backbeat (beats 2 and 4) is clearly defined. Build the intensity of the rhythm as you approach the final fill. Recommended listening: Runrig/Clannad and Riverdance.

Dave Odart   Exercise no. 3

This march-based study incorporates five, seven and nine stroke rolls. The flam and drag rudiments should use alternate sticking and must be crisp and cleanly executed in a tight, military snare drum style. The sticking, where marked, can be reversed for left handed players. Recommended listening: Steve Gadd.

Adam Double/
George Double   Need I Remind You?

This is a contemporary pop rock tune, broadly in the style of Reef and Foo Fighters.

There is a gradual dynamic build through the song and early playing should sit supportively under the vocal while remaining rich and full in tone. When the chorus begins, play with energy and projection and count carefully to ensure that hands and feet are neatly aligned and that time remains steady with the track.

Dave Holland/
Matt McDonough   Party People

Party People has a tight, funky feel with a disco backbeat (accented beats 2 and 4) in each chorus. In order to create a 'tight' feel, each note should be played to its exact length – no shorter and no longer, and beats 2 and 4 on the snare should sound punchy and purposeful.

The chorus' disco groove is built up using an open hi hat on each off-beat quaver/eighth note, the snare on beats 2 and 4 and a bass drum played on each crotchet/quarter note. This bass drum pattern is typically called 'four-to-the-floor'. It is important that the off-beat hi hats are shut immediately on the following beat, before opening again.

Disco is, of course, dance music so ensure that the playing sounds confident and stylistic. Listen to Rose Royce's *Car Wash* and *Boogie Oogie Oogie* by A Taste Of Honey for guidance.

Matt McDonough   Reggae Muffin

Reggae Muffin features a swung reggae 'one-drop' groove. This pattern was made popular by drummer Carlton Barrett, who was a member of Bob Marley and The Wailers and leaves a gap beneath the hi hat on the first beat of the bar where one might expect a bass drum.

In order to create a bouncy, shuffle feel, there should be a noticeable contrast between the accented down-beats and the non-accented off-beats in the hi hat part. Pay attention to the open/closed directions for hi hat too, these should be executed smoothly within the time patterns and try to ensure that the accent on beat 3 is heard as one unison note, across each limb.

Throughout the piece, a number of fills are started with a drag on the snare drum, a stylistic technique used in reggae drumming. The triplet quaver/eighth note fill in bar 60 should sound like a smooth run down the tom toms, with each single stroke note played at an equal volume. Further to this, the performer may find that playing the triplet crotchets/quarter notes in bar 64 with the right hand alone, will aid in the timing and accuracy of the fills around the tom toms.

Ralph Salmins   Way Cool

This is an Indie rock piece inspired by the Glaswegian, platinum-selling band Franz Ferdinand. The piece is written in chart form and is designed to be a realistic reflection of what is often found in a recording session. The chart uses repeat marks, repeat sections and variations of the bass drum pattern under a repeat mark (an often-used and tidy way of notating changes under a groove). The style is loose, relaxed rock, played at mf – ff. Solo fills are ad. lib. and designed to be improvised. Have fun and don't forget to dig in and get a big, fat sound from the drums.

Andrew Tween   Muddy Boots

Establish the slow tempo of this piece in your mind before you begin playing. Give each note its full value, maintaining good time and resisting the temptation to speed up or slow down. The opening dynamic should allow room for a contrasting build into letter A, at which point the hi hats should be allowed to 'sizzle' over the duration of each beat. This requires good left foot control.

Tom Gregory   Meditation

This piece is a set of variations based around one classic hip hop groove. It introduces a number of ways to add interest to your groove playing, without resorting to fills. Playing the snare backbeat as a flam adds huge power and purpose to the groove. The few 'fills' in the study are classic Hip hop too; they're more about space than tricky playing.

The dynamics from bar 9 should be as contrasting as possible; the f tom fill in bar 10 should explode out of the tiny p cross stick groove. Bars 10 and 12 both feature the open hi hat used as a crash, playing the snare simultaneously adds power to all these crashes. Try playing the crashes with your RH and the open hi hat with your LH (use your free hand to play the snare), this lets you put plenty of power into the hits; don't forget to make the bass drum hit just as loud.

The last four bars are inspired by the drumming of Ahmir '?uestlove' Thompson of the band The Roots on the track *You Got Me*; just as the song seems to be over, the drums return with a tense, double-time feel. In *Meditation* the feeling is more raucous; a final double-time burst of fire and energy before the tune seems to trail off and die in the final bar.

Grade 4

Dave Odart   Exercise no. 1

This waltz should be played lightly but dynamically where indicated. The double strokes in bars 3–4 should be ghosted to allow the fill to breathe. The flam accent and flamacue fills should build up to a big finish. Matt Johnson's playing on Jeff Buckley's album *Grace* gives good guidance on this style and touch.

Dave Odart   Exercise no. 2

Aim for a smooth buzz roll using semiquavers/sixteenth notes to start this study which should blend seamlessly into the singles strokes at bar 2. The double paradiddle should compliment the $\frac{12}{8}$ blues feel nicely without becoming dominant or overpowering.

Observe the ghost notes carefully and try to ensure that the change to paradiddle-diddles in the final bar is smooth with no tempo fluctuations.

Dave Odart   Exercise no. 3

This should really groove with a big backbeat to secure the pulse in the paradiddle section. Play with purpose and projection to create excitement in this exercise. Listen to the playing of Steve Smith and Clyde Stubblefield for inspiration.

Alfred James 'Pee Wee' Ellis
arr. Andrew Tween   The Chicken

The Chicken, written by band leader and saxophone player 'Pee Wee' Ellis, was made famous by bass player Jaco Pastorius. Built around strong riffs, the solo section uses the same form as the 'head' (main tune). There are many approaches that can be taken to playing this piece. During the saxophone solo (the repeat of letter A), there is the potential to open out onto the ride cymbal after the dominant semiquaver/sixteenth note figure on the hi hat during the 'head'.

The B section is an added arrangement calling on the style of bands such as The Meters and The JB Horns. At letter B the semiquaver/sixteenth note pattern, whilst still hand to hand, differs in that the left hand moves to the snare playing 'ghost notes' (small stick movements). The syncopated riffs played by the band are also punctuated by the drums. Accuracy in playing is essential for this to sound tight.

Quincy Jones
arr. George Double   Soul Bossa Nova

A big hit for composer and arranger Quincy Jones, this number is best known as the theme tune for the Austin Powers movie series, and is full of quirky good humour. This arrangement explores different Bossa Nova ideas and requires the addition of a cowbell to the standard kit set up. Ensure that the cowbell is situated in a convenient playing position, ideally on a bracket at the top of the bass drum hoop, directly above the pedal.

Henry 'Hank' Mobley
arr. George Double   Soul Station

This soul-jazz hit was penned by saxophonist 'Hank' Mobley, and was the title track of his 1960 album, released on Blue Note Records.

Try to differentiate between different feels; holding steady on the two-in-a-bar sections to create tension and then moving up a gear during the shuffle groove and in the four-in-a-bar passages. The phrasing marks should be realised stylistically; listen to Art Blakey on the original recording for inspiration, as well as Philly Joe Jones and Max Roach on other recordings from the same period. Keep ruffs crisp, always moving towards the main note to keep the tempo strict.

Pete Riley/
Andy Staples   The Spark, The Flame

The Spark, The Flame is a contemporary rock tune based on the style of hard-hitting bands Paramore and Foo Fighters. The drum part makes use of syncopated two-bar grooves, half-time patterns, groove ideas on the toms as well as seven stroke rolls on the snare at letter C1. Ensure that the sound is full and well projected whilst creating clear dynamic contrasts.

In the solo section, observe the marked hits and be stylistic in terms of dynamics and intensity. Recommended listening includes Zak Farro, Ilan Rubin, Dave Grohl and Taylor Hawkins, leading players in this genre.

Neil Robinson   Ali's Boogaloo

Boogaloo music originated in New York and is a fusion of African-American R&B, Soul and Latin music. This piece evokes this style with a funky/soul main groove and Latin-style phrased stops. Recommended listening would be Lou Donaldson's *Alligator Boogaloo*, especially the 1970 live version which starts with a classic Boogaloo-style drum solo.

Matt McDonough   The Amgard Corps

This piece is based on a $\frac{6}{8}$ March, which is also known as a compound time signature. The opening should be played very straight and with a spirit that captures a marching band on the parade square.

We enter the section at bar 17 with a double stroke crescendo roll. This brings us into a groovier section, whereby any non-accented notes should be played almost as background 'ghosted' notes. It is up to the performer as to how they stick the non-directed notes, however, any notes with directions above them should be followed. Think of this section as a passage which focuses on a groove aspect, using the flams as a type of backbeat.

Bar 33 sees a section which moves around the tom toms, whilst keeping the non-accented snare drum notes continuously bubbling underneath. This section can be played hand to hand (R, L, R, L etc.) or by keeping the left hand on the snare drum and using the right hand to move around the toms. Depending on the crash cymbal placement, the performer may, at bars 49–50, decide to play the crash cymbals with the left hand.

Bars 51–52, 55 and 59–60 should be played as a strict five stroke roll with a clean accent on the third quaver/eighth note. Note the alternating sticking of each roll. Observe the extreme change in dynamics; at the end of bar 64 down to *p* and then *ff* at bar 72 where the performer has the opportunity to play out the piece with a stylistically typical strong and loud marching band pattern.

Grade 3 Rudiments

You will need to learn the rudiments up to Grade 2 and the following to be able to play the Grade 3 Exercises.

Five stroke roll

Seven stroke roll

Nine stroke roll

Note that the tempo must be increased to establish rebounded rolls.

Candidates must prepare all three exercises, but only two will be played during the exam.
One is chosen by the candidate, the other by the examiner.
(If you are left handed you may reverse the sticking.)

Grade 3 Exercises
Exercise no. 1

Dave Odart

Remember to look at the Performance Notes on pages 5-8

Exercise no. 2

Dave Odart

Exercise no. 3

Dave Odart

Remember to look at the Performance Notes on pages 5-8

Track 1 – Demo
Track 2 – With click
Track 3 – Without click

Need I Remind You?

Adam Double/George Double

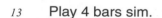

Remember to look at the Performance Notes on pages 5-8

Track 4 – Demo
Track 5 – With click
Track 6 – Without click

Party People

Dave Holland/Matt McDonough

Tight funky disco ♩ = 125

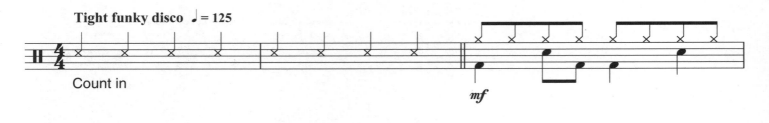

Count in

mf

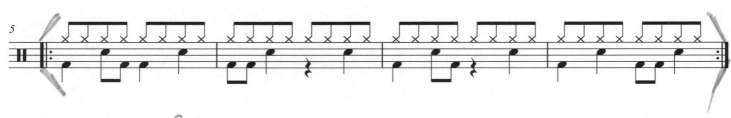

Disco feel

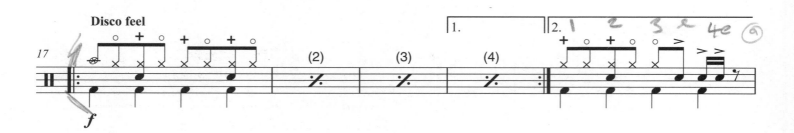

f

Track 7 – Demo
Track 8 – With click
Track 9 – Without click

Reggae Muffin

Matt McDonough

Remember to look at the Performance Notes on pages 5-8

Choke
(not rushed)

Way Cool

Ralph Salmins

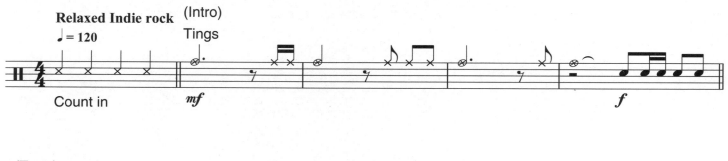

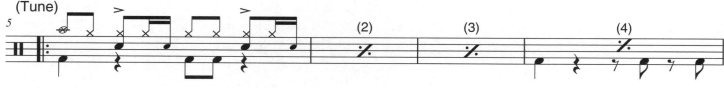

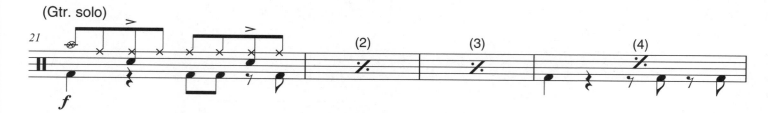

Remember to look at the Performance Notes on pages 5-8

Muddy Boots

Andrew Tween

Remember to look at the Performance Notes on pages 5-8

Meditation

Tom Gregory

Remember to look at the Performance Notes on pages 5-8

Grade 4 Rudiments

You will need to learn the rudiments up to Grade 3 and the following to be able to play the Grade 4 Exercises.

Flam tap

Flam accent

Flamacue

Flam paradiddle

Double paradiddle

Paradiddle-diddle

Candidates must prepare all three exercises, but only two will be played during the exam.
One is chosen by the candidate, the other by the examiner.
(If you are left handed you may reverse the sticking.)

Grade 4 Exercises
Exercise no. 1

Dave Odart

Remember to look at the Performance Notes on pages 5-8

Exercise no. 2

Dave Odart

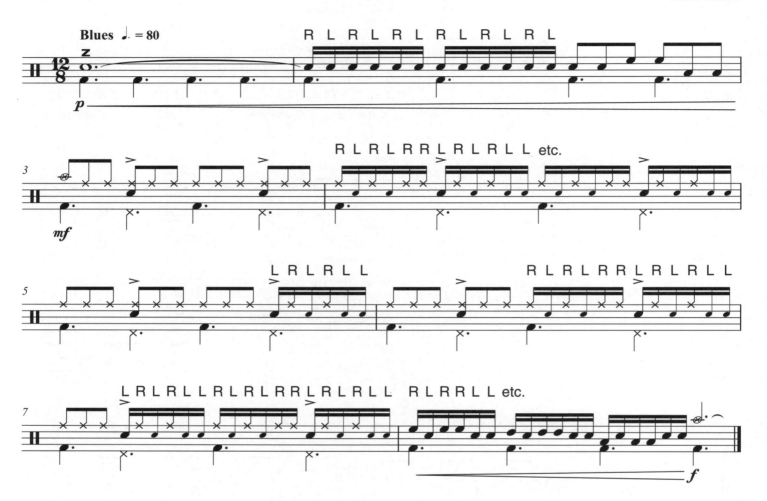

Remember to look at the Performance Notes on pages 5-8

Exercise no. 3

Dave Odart

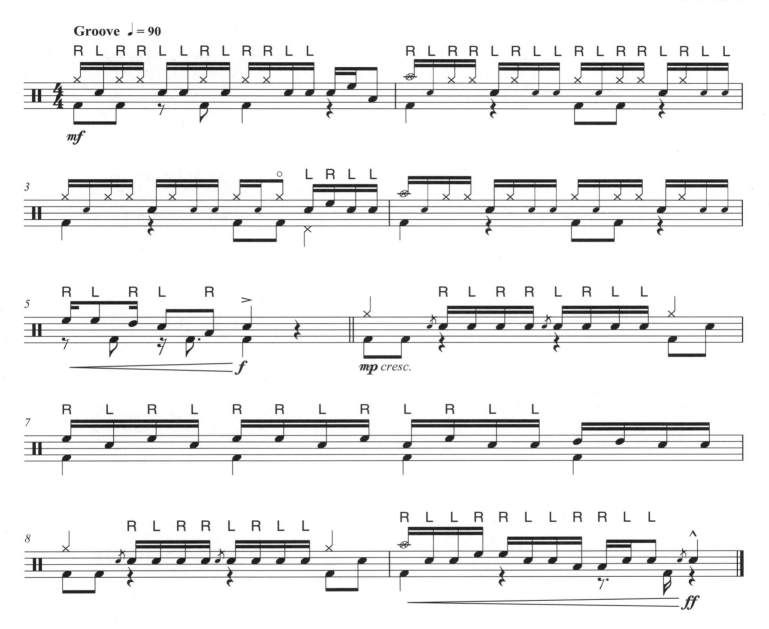

Remember to look at the Performance Notes on pages 5-8

Track 13 – Demo
Track 14 – With click
Track 15 – Without click

The Chicken

Alfred James 'Pee Wee' Ellis
arr. Andrew Tween

(Melody 1st time, sax solo 2nd time –
cont. sim. /open out)

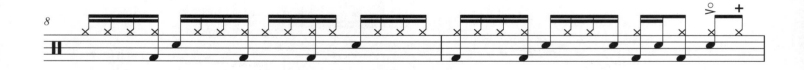

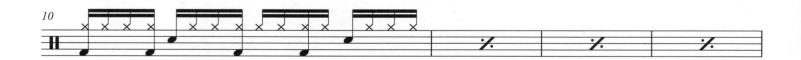

Track 16 – Demo
Track 17 – With click
Track 18 – Without click

Soul Bossa Nova

Quincy Jones
arr. George Double

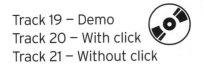

Soul Station

Henry 'Hank' Mobley
arr. George Double

4-feel, ad lib. time
(Piano and drums trade 2-bar phrases)

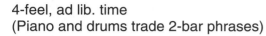

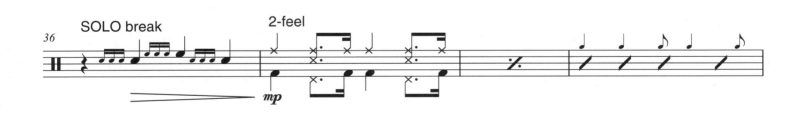

Remember to look at the Performance Notes on pages 5-8

The Spark, The Flame

Pete Riley/Andy Staples

Remember to look at the Performance Notes on pages 5-8

Ali's Boogaloo

Neil Robinson

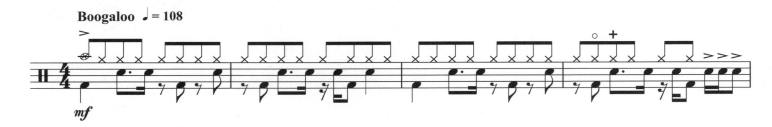

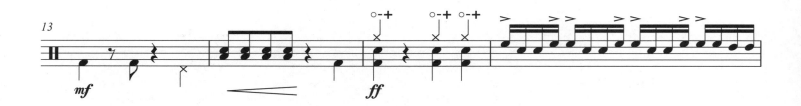

Remember to look at the Performance Notes on pages 5-8

The Amgard Corps

Matt McDonough

Remember to look at the Performance Notes on pages 5-8